NOISY
Animal
ABC

www.francesmackay.com

Design by Nicky Scott
www.nickyscottdesign.com
Illustrations supplied by Dreamstime

ISBN 978-0-646-85207-2

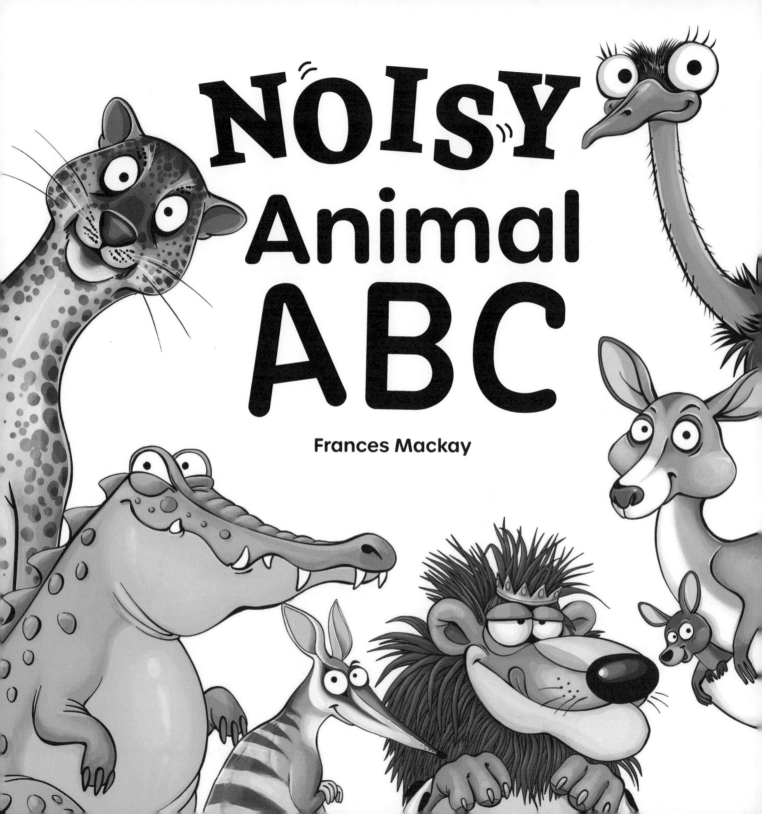

NOISY
Animal
ABC

Frances Mackay

Aa
is for ALLIGATOR

SNAP!
SNAP!
SNAP!

BUZZZZZZZZZ

Bb is for BEE

Cc is for CAT

D d is for DOG

STOMP!
STOMP!
STOMP!

Ee is for ELEPHANT

F f is for FROG

RIBBIT!
RIBBIT!
RIBBIT!

RIBBIT!
RIBBIT!
RIBBIT!

G g is for GOOSE

HONK! HONK!

HONK!

Hh is for HUMAN

Jj is for JAGUAR

GRRROWL

ZZZZZZZzz

Shhhhhhh!

Kk is for KOALA

L l is for LION

Mm
is for MONKEY

Nn is for NUMBAT

CLICK! CLICK!

OOOH!
OOOH!

Oo
is for ORANGUTAN

Pp is for PARROT

Qq is for QUOKKA

HOP HOP HOP

Rr is for RAT

SQUEEK!
SQUEEK!
SQUEEK!

BOING! BOING! BOING! BOING!

S s is for SPIDER

T t is for TURKEY

GOBBLE! GOBBLE!

U u is for UMBRELLABIRD

OOOOM!
OOOOM!

Ww is for WHALE

Xx is for X-RAY FISH

Yy is for YAK

GRUNT!
GRUNT!

Zz is for ZEBRA

A-AH!
A-AH!

BYE!
BYE!

Printed in Great Britain
by Amazon